Ali lives in Istanbul,
a big city in Turkey. He lives
in an old building near the famous
Blue Mosque. After school, Ali comes
home and sits at the window. He looks
at the boats. They are going out to sea.

'What are you doing?' Ali's mother asks.

'I'm taking photos of those boats,' Ali says.

His mother looks at him and laughs. 'Photos?
How can you take photos? You haven't got a camera!'

'I know that, Mother! I'm taking photos in my head.
I can see the photos here!'

Ali shows a place near his eyes. His mother laughs again.

'Stop talking and go to your father's shop!' she tells him.

1

Ali's father sells vegetables and fruit. Ali works in the shop after school.

'Don't move. Stand there near the door!' Ali says suddenly.

'Why?' his father asks.

'I want to take your photo!'

Ali's father smiles. 'My photo? First, get a camera. Then you can take my photo!'

'Buy me a camera!' Ali says.

Ali's father stops smiling. 'I haven't got any money for cameras,' he says slowly.

Every afternoon, Ali walks in the old city of Istanbul. He looks at the houses near the water. Some houses are very old. He watches the men on the bridge. They are catching fish. He watches the boats. He watches, and he sees photos in his head.

'How can I get a camera?' he thinks. Suddenly, he has the answer. 'I'm going to work in the market!'

There is an old market
near Ali's school. There are
small shops in the market.
People buy and sell food there.

Ali goes there every afternoon after school.
He works with a smile. He carries bags for people.
People like him and they give him money. He puts it in
his pocket.

'One day I'm going to have a lot of money,' Ali says to his
mother. 'Then I can buy a camera. And then I'm going to
take a photo of you in the kitchen.'

'No, not in the kitchen! On the balcony, with your
father,' his mother says.

'No, not on the balcony – in my shop,' his father says.

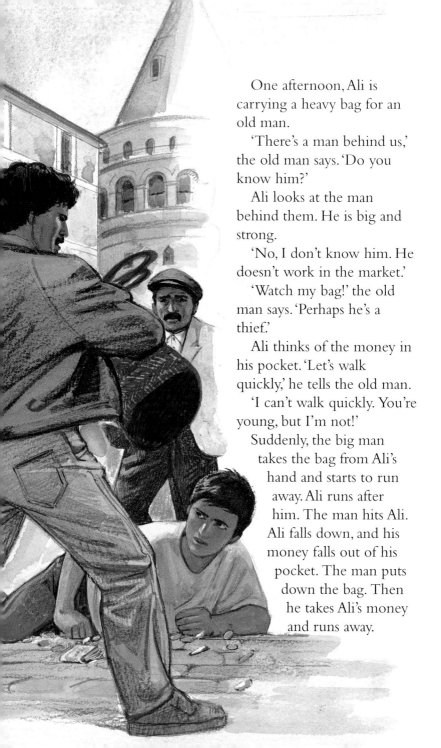

One afternoon, Ali is carrying a heavy bag for an old man.

'There's a man behind us,' the old man says. 'Do you know him?'

Ali looks at the man behind them. He is big and strong.

'No, I don't know him. He doesn't work in the market.'

'Watch my bag!' the old man says. 'Perhaps he's a thief.'

Ali thinks of the money in his pocket. 'Let's walk quickly,' he tells the old man.

'I can't walk quickly. You're young, but I'm not!'

Suddenly, the big man takes the bag from Ali's hand and starts to run away. Ali runs after him. The man hits Ali. Ali falls down, and his money falls out of his pocket. The man puts down the bag. Then he takes Ali's money and runs away.

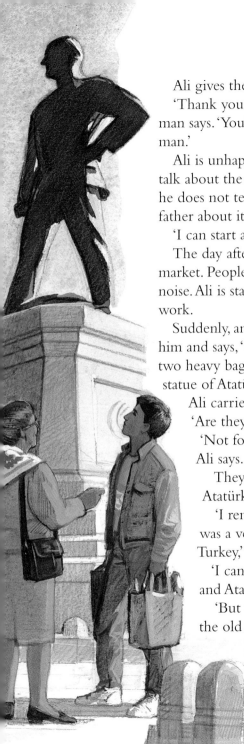

Ali gives the bag to the old man.

'Thank you very much,' the old man says. 'You're a very good young man.'

Ali is unhappy, but he does not talk about the money. That evening, he does not tell his mother and father about it.

'I can start again,' he thinks.

The day after that, Ali is at the market. People are making a lot of noise. Ali is standing and waiting for work.

Suddenly, an old woman comes to him and says, 'Can you carry my two heavy bags? I live near the statue of Atatürk.'

Ali carries them for her.

'Are they very heavy?' she asks.

'Not for me. I'm very strong,' Ali says.

They arrive at the statue of Atatürk.

'I remember Atatürk. He was a very important man for Turkey,' the old woman says.

'I can take a photo of you and Atatürk,' Ali says.

'But where's your camera?' the old woman asks.

'I haven't got a camera,' Ali says.

The old woman looks at him. Then she smiles.

'All right. Take my photo without a camera. But wait. First, I'm going to do my hair,' she says.

They come to the old woman's street. Ali carries the bags up to her flat. It is a big flat, with a lot of pictures.

'How much money do you want?' the old woman asks.

'How much do you want to give me?' Ali answers.

'Sit here and wait,' she says.

She goes into a small room and comes back with a camera in her hand.

'This was my son's first camera. Take it,' she says.

Ali looks at the camera
for a long time. He takes it
in his hand.

Then he gives it back to the old woman.

'It's a beautiful camera. I . . . I can't take it,'
he says.

She takes Ali's hand and puts the camera in it again.

'My son doesn't want it. He has a new camera now.'

'You're very good to me. How can I thank you?' Ali says.

'Come again one day and take my photo. A real photo.
And here's some money for today.'

'I can't take your money. But I can carry your bags from
the market again,' Ali says.

'You're a good boy. Remember my name. It's Mrs Yildiz,'
she tells him.

'Of course, Mrs Yildiz,' Ali says.

'Goodbye, Ali. Take good photos with my son's camera.'

Ali runs home and tells his mother about Mrs Yildiz and the camera.

'Does it work?' his mother says.

'Yes, it works. I'm going to take your photo now,' Ali answers.

'But there's no film in it, son,' his mother says. She gives him some money. 'Go and buy some film. And I want to buy a new dress. Then you can take my photo.'

'Thank you,' he says. 'But I want to buy film with *my* money, not *yours*.'

Ali works every day in the market after school. Every evening he comes home late.

'This is difficult,' he thinks. 'People do a lot of work for very little money.'

But one day, Ali has the money for some film. 'I can take *real* photos now,' he thinks.

Ali remembers Mrs Yildiz and goes to her flat. She opens the door and sees him. She is very happy.

'I want to take your photo, Mrs Yildiz,' Ali says.

She takes Ali into the kitchen. A tall man is drinking coffee there.

'This is my son, Yusuf. Take a photo of me with him. Come, Yusuf. Sit here with me.'

'Smile, please,' Ali says, and he takes their photo.

'Yusuf works for a newspaper. He can teach you about photos,' Mrs Yildiz says.

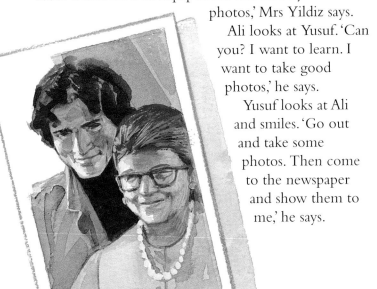

Ali looks at Yusuf. 'Can you? I want to learn. I want to take good photos,' he says.

Yusuf looks at Ali and smiles. 'Go out and take some photos. Then come to the newspaper and show them to me,' he says.

'I'm going to take a lot of photos. They're all in my head now,' Ali says.

Ali walks in the streets of Istanbul. Suddenly, the city looks very beautiful. He takes photos of bridges and boats and old mosques. He takes photos of people in the streets and in shops.

Then, one day, he goes to see Yusuf at the newspaper.

Yusuf looks at the photos. 'Hmm, not bad,' he says.

'Not bad?' Ali says.

'Yes. Not bad. Your photos are not bad.'

'They aren't good?'

'Some of the photos are good, but some of them aren't,' Yusuf tells Ali.

Ali is not happy about this. Suddenly, he says, 'Give me my photos, please.' He is angry, but Yusuf does not understand.

Ali goes home. He tells his mother about Yusuf and the photos.

'You weren't very clever, Ali,' she says. 'You aren't a famous photographer.'

Ali is unhappy. 'Sometimes I open my mouth and I don't think first,' he says.

'Go to Yusuf. You're sorry. Tell him that.'

'I can't go now,' Ali answers. 'I can't. I'm angry.'

He walks in the streets. 'Why did I walk away from Yusuf?' he thinks. 'It wasn't clever. Why didn't I think first? Why...?'

Suddenly, he sees a small photography shop. He goes in. An old man is sitting at a table. He has a happy face. His name is Selim.

'I like your shop. You have beautiful cameras. I want to work here,' Ali says.

'I can't give you any money,' the old man answers.

'I don't want money. I want to learn about photography,' Ali says.

'Look at my photos, please,' Ali says.

Selim looks at them and then he says, 'We all see with our eyes. But good photographers see things with the eye of the camera.'

Ali starts to learn. He takes photos of people. He takes photos of doors and windows. 'Doors and windows are alive, too,' Selim says.

Ali sees a lot of young children in the city. They work in shops, or they sell fruit, cold drinks and newspapers in the streets. Ali takes photos of them, too. There are smiles on their faces, but their eyes are not smiling.

Ali shows Selim his new photos. 'Do you like them?'

'Yes,' Selim says. 'You're learning. You're building photos.'

'When can I sell my photos to a newspaper?' Ali asks.

'Wait,' Selim answers.

Ali works at the market after school. He always wants money for film. He takes photos of the people at the market, too.

Early one Saturday morning, he sees some young children on a bridge. They have big, unhappy eyes and they are fishing. Ali takes a photo of them.

He goes to Selim's flat, in the old city, and he shows Selim the photo of the children on the bridge. Selim looks at it for a long time.

'Yes,' he says. 'You're learning quickly!'

'You're very good to me, Mr Selim. You're my teacher.'

'I like teaching you. You're a son to me,' Selim says.

One day, Ali sees Mrs Yildiz again, but he walks away quickly. He does not want to see her.

'Ali, Ali! Why are you running away?' she asks.

Ali stops. 'I'm not very clever,' he says. 'Did Yusuf tell you?'

He tells her about that day in Yusuf's office at the newspaper. 'I'm sorry now,' he says.

'What are you talking about?' Mrs Yildiz says. 'Don't you know? One of your photos is in the newspaper today!'

'My photo? In the newspaper? Which photo?'

'There are two children on a bridge. They're catching a big fish.'

'Oh, Mrs Yildiz, I'm very happy,' Ali says, and he laughs happily. 'Can I carry your bags for you now?'

'No, thank you. Go home now,' she says.

Ali runs to Selim's shop.

'My photo's in the newspaper!' he tells him.

'Yes, here it is,' Selim says, and he shows Ali the newspaper.

'I don't understand! How...? Who...?' Selim is smiling. 'It was you! You showed my photo to Yusuf!'

Selim smiles again. Then he says, 'But you can't stop learning.'

'Yes, you're right,' Ali says.

'Tomorrow is a very important day for you.'

Ali doesn't understand. 'Tomorrow? Why is tomorrow important?'

'The newspaper has a job for a young person,' Selim tells him. 'That person is going to learn about photography. And that young person is you. You're going to start your new job tomorrow.'

They laugh and laugh.

ACTIVITIES

Pages 1–7

Before you read

1 What do you know about Turkey? How many towns can you name? How many buildings? Can you name a famous river?

2 Look at the Word List at the back of the book and talk about these questions.

   a Which of these do you have in your town? Where are they?

      a bridge   a market   a mosque   a statue

   b Which of these can't you buy in a shop?

      a camera   a city   a fish   vegetables

   c What can't you do with a bag?

      carry it   sell it   show it   tell it

While you read

3 Who is talking or thinking?

   a 'How can you take photos? You haven't got a camera.'   ....

   b 'I haven't got any money for cameras.'   ....

   c 'I'm going to work in the market!'   ....

   d 'Watch my bag! Perhaps he's a thief.'   ....

   e 'I can take a photo of you and Atatürk.'   ....

   f 'This was my son's first camera. Take it.'   ....

After you read

4 Work with a friend.

   Student A: You are Ali's friend. He has a new camera. Ask him about it.

   Student B: You are Ali. Answer your friend's questions.

5 What is Ali going to do with his camera?

Pages 8–15

Before you read

6 Answer the questions. What do you think?

   a Who are the people in the colour photos on pages 8 and 9?

   b What are they saying?

While you read

7 Finish the sentences. Write one word.

   a Ali .... his mother about the camera.

   b He works in the market and then buys some ....

   c He meets Mrs Yildiz's .... , Yusuf.

   d Yusuf works for a ....

   e Ali .... his photos to Yusuf.

   f He gets .... because Yusuf doesn't like all of them.

   g Ali gets a job in a .... shop.

   h He .... from Selim and starts to take good photos.

   i Selim and Yusuf like his photo of some children on a ....

   j Ali is going to work for the ....

After you read

8 Write, for the newspaper, about the two children in Ali's photo. How old are they? What do they do? Why are they unhappy?

9 Write about two of these people. What do they do in the story for Ali and his photography?

his mother   his father   Mrs Yildiz   Yusuf   Selim

WORD LIST *with example sentences*

alive (adj) Two of the men in the car were dead, but one was *alive*.

balcony (n) We can walk from our bedroom onto a big *balcony*.

bridge (n) There are two *bridges* across the river. One is for cars and one is for trains.

camera (n) I want to take a picture of that building. Have you got a *camera*?

carry (v) Is your bag heavy? Can I *carry* it for you?

city (n) We live in a small town, but we like visiting big *cities* on holiday.

fish (n/v) I am going to catch some *fish*, and we can eat them this evening.

laugh (v) She never stops *laughing*. She is a very happy child.

learn (v) We are *learning* English because we want to visit London.

market (n) I don't buy fruit from a shop because there is a *market* every Saturday in my town.

mosque (n) Istanbul has a lot of famous *mosques*. I visited Hagia Sophia and the Blue Mosque.

pocket (n) Have you got any money in your coat *pocket*?

real (adj) He isn't a *real* friend. He wants your money.

sell (v) We want to *sell* our house and move to a small flat.

show (v) Is that a new dress in your bag? *Show* me!

statue (n) There are *statues* of famous people in the gardens.

tell (v) They *tell* interesting stories about their years in India.

thief (n) *Thieves* are taking bags from trains at night.

vegetable (n) I only eat fruit and *vegetables*, because I don't want to eat dead animals.

without (prep) They are buying a house *without* a garden.

Pearson Education Limited
Edinburgh Gate, Harlow,
Essex CM20 2JE, England
and Associated Companies throughout the world.

ISBN: 978-1-4058-7666-7

First published 2000
This edition first published 2008

13

Copyright © Pearson Education Ltd 2008
Illustrations by Chris Molan

Typeset by Graphicraft Ltd, Hong Kong
Set in 12/14pt Bembo
Printed in China
SWTC/13

Published by Pearson Education Ltd

Every effort has been made to trace the copyright holders and we apologise in advance for any
unintentional omissions. We would be pleased to insert the appropriate acknowledgement in any
subsequent edition of this publication.

For a complete list of the titles available in the Pearson English Readers series, please
visit www.pearsonenglishreaders.com. Alternatively, write to your local Pearson Education
office or to Pearson English Readers Marketing Department, Pearson Education,
Edinburgh Gate, Harlow, Essex CM20 2JE, England.